Cheerful Hearts

Award-Winning Author
Wayne Lindsey

Other books by

Wayne Lindsey

The Love Response-Helper

Golden Purposes Of Life

Evil Lives Within

A special message from the Author

Hello, my dear beloved reading fans! There's a unique person wanted, a true champion and how fortunate! you are the very person!

Who wants to see you exercise your uniqueness? This bountiful, busy, beautiful, world wants you to assert your unique being, and I really do not see how it is going to get on well without you not believing that you're unique, a special star. It has awaited your coming for so long, and has kept in store so many golden opportunities for you to improve, be cheerful, be kind, passionate, be fun loving, happy, creative, adventurous, self-confident, ecstatic and blissful about yourself. It will be disappointing if, when the proper time arrives, you do not smilingly lay hold and do something worthwhile about your uniqueness.

How can we make life yield its fullest and unique best in us? How can we know the true secret of being ecstatic beings? How can we attain true and lasting greatness? How can we fill the whole of life with happiness, peace, love, a joy, a satisfaction that is ever prosperous and abiding, that ever increases, never diminishes, that imparts to it a sparkle that never loses its lustre, that ever fascinates, never wearies?

And especially to those students whose teacher disrespectfully tells them that "you're no good. Your employer will say we can't use you, we have to let you go, it doesn't matter how many hours of CPD busing you've got." Dear student, ignore the teacher. Lift up your head and hold it up high and aim for your prize. Remove the doubts from your mind and strive for your goal.

Sky's the limit when you can be what you want. You can become the next Physician, Scientist, Barrister, Nurse, Astronauts, prime minister or president of tomorrow. The teacher will one day ask for your friendship. Don't wait for luck, be driven and dedicated, step up in life and achieve your innovative visions.You can go on and be one of the greatest, don't just do it for your pride, do it for your name, you never know it may be inducted into the hall of fame.

Mother nature truly believes that we are born true champions. Even when you rob and kill she loves you still. Mother nature knows that times are getting harder, Still she wants you to keep striving for better. Don't be discouraged by the pitfalls and hard challenges and the numerous troubles in this world that's part of life, pain endures for the night but joy will come in the morning. Some people have to fight, some people give it up, but not you because you were born a champion. Always try and keep feeling the success of hunger in your tummy. Cherish your visions; cherish your ideals; cherish the music that stirs in your heart, the beauty that forms in your mind, the loveliness that drapes your purest thoughts. Mother nature does not not say we need to be happy everyday, no human has ever done it and no one ever will.

Envy no one; envy breeds bitterness. The person you would envy has their own sorrows and shadows too. You see them when the sunlight is on their face; you don't see the person when the person is in shadow-land. My beloved fellow beings, someday we'll put it together and get it all done, and eventually walk in the rays of a beautiful sun. Put yourself in harmony with nature, realize the wonderful force of your will, and you will be robust, a genuine king or queen among men.

As much as possible try to avoid loud, aggressive people who love to quarrel, for quarrels and aggressiveness rest in the hearts of fools.

Let's see if this book passes the test. If it's true that mother nature wants us to be more blissful, be more cheerful, live healthily, exercise regular, develop positive mindset on earth And if so, rejoice that we have found it to be true, lay hold of it, build upon it, and tell others of it. This is an expression of one of the greatest truths, of one of the greatest factors of this world that we are special, unique human beings.

Love cheers us

The morning was glowing, clear, cool; there was a sweet, dry sharpness in the air; brown-tailed Rabbits bounded out of the open spaces; and the spherical, glistening hills, with their bold, Green meadow slopes, over shadowed the close foot paths. The sky was outline by a few clouds. Beautiful Green leaves inclining upward in their spring style.

Many stories of merriment, romance, cheerfulness, laughter, joy. Were written for the young adults ones of my time, and they gave me so much pleasure, and aroused such a new interest in to what makes us human cheerful that it has seemed wise to write this little book of cheerful hearts and send them out to a wider circle of adults males and females.

Spring and summer had been a light-hearted time in my younger days. It had been a hectic time, too, and from daybreak until duskiness the chirping and humming of the merry people there had mix with the rustle of the leaves, and the delicate swish, of the tall grass, as the wind passed over it.The beating of waves on sandy beaches. We cherished the cool summer breeze. Children building sand castles and having fun.

The truth is, there had been a few disputations, and some undesirable things to remember, but I can't forget reading romance and cheerful stories enough to throw away all the dismal memories and keep only the cheerful ones, and start writing this little book.

A few love songs that cheered my heart was All the love in the world. Two lines of that song I'm particularly fond of are. My love is stronger, and my love is true. I truly believe that love is a true healing power, the most powerful force in our universe, and that true love never dies no matter how hard humans try.

Another song I enjoyed singing was cherish the love. One of the most gratifying feeling in the world is to walk along the sea front with the one you truly love hand in hand, and cherish ever moment you've been given. And cherish the love you have for as long as you shall live. Yes money makes the world go run. But without love no one can truly find happiness, joy, be blissful about oneself, love conquers all. All things point to the infinite; and love more than all things else.

A short story on why love cheers our hearts

The afternoon sun was streaming in across the town, waves rippled along whites sands, small cruise afar at the bay and the long side of the sea town stretching out against the sky which looked like the end of the earth is stimulating and breathtaking to any one. It gave an eager enjoyment to Ken.

"Within fifteen minutes, maybe," Ken weighed up, as the energize odour of the salt water blew near his nostrils, "I will see Lucy soon."

Lucy was glowing and delightful with love for all who set their eyes on her

When with the crowd he had made his way off the bus, and and make is way along the platform at the Bus station, ignoring the earsplitting loud voices of the commuters, he started walking toward the beach promenade, invited by the glimpse of the turquoise sea. Hence he crossed the stores with its variety of shops flashy cars; he passed picturesque guest houses and villas where carriages and horse-carts were being driven casually between the rows of beautiful summer skyscraper, and pass through the famously block of amusements shops on the promenade. He succeeded in getting a second floor room on the sea side view of the beautiful villa where he booked. He learned from the receptionist that Lucy was not at the same villa. Sea air having arouse his appetite, Ken decided to feast before setting out in search of Lucy.

When, after his meal, he reached the mall, the flashy electric lights had already been turned on and the regular evening crowd of people was beginning to form. He strolled along now looking at the long stretch beach and the sea waves rushing to the shores, now at the mall crowd where he might perhaps at any moment behold the face of the most sunning girl in this world. He recognize instead, the face of his friend Bob

"Hello, you!" shouted Ken, giving his friend the high five. "What are you doing here? I thought your affairs would keep you in another part of the Caribbean."

"They could," replied Ken in a tone and with a look whose affliction he made little effort to hide.

"What happened?"

"What's the worry?"

Ken was silent for a moment; then he said suddenly:

"I'll talk to you about it. I need to talk to someone, it's doing my head in.

They were both silent for a while as they passed through the arcades, pavilion, and a ball room to a quieter part of the huge pier. They sat near the railing and watch people enjoying themselves in the sea. The talked for a bit, the crested band of dimness grew more and more lucid. They could see, the long borderline of dazzling lights on the mall, and the escalating crowd of people. From the line of mall lights, shone those of exotic night bars. Above these, the sky was filled with the most ravishing stars your eyes will ever see, and inexpressible beautiful. Down on the beach front were people enjoying fish and crackers, strolling near the tide line and enjoying cool refreshing beers, a group of reveller were dancing and bouncing in delight.

"It's like this,"said Bob "a few months ago I got engage"

"Oh!, I didn't know. Good wishes"

"We decided to get married in the Caribbean, and lived happily ever after, for a while, we kept in regular contact. A few weeks ago I haven't heard from her. And to be honest when a man truly loves a woman he'll give up all he's got just to be with the one he really loves. Since then I've been checking the resorts on the islands in the hope I'll find her. I suppose she was upset at something I said during a row that grew out of proportion. She want's us to live in the Caribbean, I want us to live in Africa."

"So?"

"Well, I can't locate her number isn't working and I haven't had any response from the emails I messaged her. And I'm going back to Africa next week."

"And you're still crazy in love with her?"

"Sure; that's true."

He was acceptable to hold back from attempting to reason Ken out of his devotion for the princess he's deeply in love with. He knew that in purely letting Ken confess to him the cause of his worries, he had done all that Ken would expect from any friend.

He restricted himself, therefore, to caution Ken that all men have their discontent in this life; to treating the lady annoyance as light and customary, and to cheering him up by making him join in seeing the sights of the seas side shops.

They looked on at the outside of a seaside hut, while steel band musicians played popular tunes; and watched the attractive girls leaning against the wooden shacks while the played and sing calypso songs long, "Tiny whiny" and "Wine and go down". They bought baked fish, Okra, and fritters, ate it and belched as they passed down the mall and looked at the stars and bright moonlight. Down on a bottom part of the mall they devoured jerk chicken, and in a long expensive drank refreshing beer and saw a dance show. Then they left the mall, walked to a taxi stand, where among light-hearted beer drinkers they heard the band play "Lambada dance" and after the music show, they arrived at the Villa.

Every single thing that happen that evening was favorable to Ken and cheerful enough in itself, but it won't prevented Ken that night from continuing his search for the most adorable lady in the world. He delayed the search for the next day. And when that time came, he would make the most of it

He had decided to go up to the sea view room and watch the beach and meditate. He pondered, he would, in the morning and inquire at every hotel, villas and guest houses near the beach until he should obtain news of his beloved Lucy.

He awoke the following morning the ray of the morning sun burned his sleepy eyes, when he was attracted by the shacks that where dotted on the wide beach. He went down the reception, and on to the steps of the villa to rest awhile in the shade of one of the roofs.

Although it was not yet ten AM. several people in bathing suits were making for the sea. A little Horse-cart with children aboard was passing the villas. They were singing merrily, cheerful, and shouting. Ken decided to knock on some hotel doors with a photo of Lucy. He questioned every nearby person without getting any luck. Then he resumed his stroll up the mall. He went past the lighthouse and turned back.

He had reached one of the pier without having found the most beautiful girl in the world. His eye caught a small poster. Approaching it he read it.

Lost expensive gold watch special initials, whoever return it will be handsomely rewarded.

As it happen Ken was in luck. Is feet somehow mange to kick a small object from a playing ground where swim goers where playing volleyball.

He quickly contacted the number that was on the poster. A sexy voice answered the phone. It was the nearby guest house proper-tier right next to the villa he was staying. On his arrival he was greeted with one of the most beautiful, adorable, cheerful, pleasant smile is eyes have seen in a long while.

"Thank you ever so much. I took a walk on the beach just after breakfast and dropped it somewhere. It's a bit loose on my hands."

"I picked it up near near the volley-ball court. It's a odd chance that it should be found by some one stopping at a nearby villa. But, pardon me, you're going away without mentioning the reward."

She stared at him with some awe, until she detected that he was joking. Then she smiled a smile that gave Ken quite a cheerful thrill, and said, with some tenderness of tone:

"Let the award be what you want."

"And that confer be to do what you be obliged me do."

"Oh, that would be jolly. I am quite alone here; haven't any acquaintances in this guest house. I like to go swimming and I'm rather shy about going alone."

"I'd like to have the pleasure of escorting you into the waves."

The following day Ken and the lady went swimming together at the beach close to the villa he holiday in. He realize that she was a strong swimmer. Perhaps, even a stronger swimmer than he is. Ken notice well shaped the woman body was, she was one of the most carve shapely person he'd seen in a while.

She was very cheerful, always smiling frequently after a while, they got dressed and walked to the mall, she chatted pleasingly with him.

Ken took her into the art gallery to see the all the exhibition, and she was good enough to laugh at his jokes even to the ones that sounded a bit off key. It was Ken who seem to interest her. Further down the mall they stopped at cocktail bar shack, and on the way out he Ken asked her if it were any chance he could see her again.

"As it is you who invites me, I'll give up my afternoon chores and see you."

They rode on a bus viewing and taking photographs of the most magnificent beauty, and after spending a short while drinking cocktails and listening to the steel band. They hired a skipper to take them out in his glass-bottom boat view the dolphins swimming.

Late in the evening, they sat together for a time on the pier, then walked up the mall and compared the stars with the high guiding light of the lighthouse.

He bought her chocolates at a confectioner's store. Assuredly, been hesitant to end the evening, they stood for some minutes predisposition against the mall railing, listening to the waves of the sea and watching the beam of stars and moonlight stretching from beach to the scope.

It was not until he was alone in his room that Ken re-imagine of his abandon of the loveliest girl in the world Lucy. And regretful as he was, he did not form any distinct disparate of resuming his search for her the next day. He rather cheered himself on not having met her while he was with this enchanting lady he just met Rosie.

And he passed next day also with the enchanting Rosie. They sat on the balcony together reading various magazine and sun bathing for a while after breakfast; went to the pier, then near to a small waterfall where they spent another hour making the weights slide along the sanded board and then took another beach swim.

After enjoying a nice picnic they walked back up to the mall and then to the pier.

Seeing a small boat there, bouncing up and down in the waves, Rosie asked:

"Wonder if the boat skipper would take us in his boat for a while?"

Ken went down to the sea front and shouted to the boat skipper, who was more than happy to obliged he needed the money. The skipper brought the boat ashore and set sailing slowly.

"This is a lovely beach for husbands and wife's this summer," remarked the skipper in a chirpy way.

Rosie looked at Ken with a crimson face and laugh. Ken was pleased at seeing that she seemed not displeased.

"We're not married," said Ken

"Not yet," said the skipper with cheerful winks, and then he gave out a very tickling laughter.

On they return, they became very affectionate. They decided to go to the local indoor go-kart race track. Half a mile from the mall. He found himself quite unconcerned to the crowd of people. The loveliest girl in the world Lucy might have passed him a few times without attracting his attention. He had eyes firmly on Rosie.

And that very night, far from blaming himself for his conduct toward the beautiful Lucy, he rarely thought of her at all, more than to ponder about what good fortune he had avoided meeting up with her. Some of the guests at the villa thought Ken and Rosie where a couple, the two were seen constantly together. Other guest thought they were engaged.

Ken spoke of this to her next morning as they were being whirled the town center away from the scenery of smooth beach and lovely palm trees.

"A lady asked me whilst we were on the balcony if we where on our honeymoon" he said.

"Well, what if you were?"

They stroll through the town center leisurely, and did a bit of craft shopping. They passed most of that midday in a shopping mall, evidently watching the crowd.

Ken and Rosie was enjoying some fried fish, looking down at the happy tourist and residents enjoying the cool sea breeze when Bob in bathing trunks and with his swimming machine. The tall, muscular Bob greeted Ken politely.

"What's up man?" said Bob." "Nice to see you here."

They chatted briefly before Bob took his departure.

Rosie and Ken walked left the food takeaway and restaurant in silence.

"Bet you, Bob's thinking I'm seeing you."

She replied softly

"I would be willing if I were certain of one thing."

"What's the one thing?"

"That you're not seeing any other woman."

That evening, after a meal, Ken and Rosie where chatting and laughing on the villa balcony, when a man appeared at the bottom.

"Why, Ken old boy, I'm glad to see you. Let me introduce you to my brother fiance."

Ken stood still and stared. Rosie, too, remained motionless. After a moment, Ken said very quietly

"You're mistaken. Aren't you?"

Ken looked at Rosie. She turned her blue eyes fearlessly on Bob

"You, bastard," she said. "I'm sorry about all this, Ken. I really like you. Good-bye."

She ran back into the hotel and arranged to make her departure on an early bus the next day.

Ken turned toward the mall, looking quite bewildered, Bob unintentionally followed him. After a period of silence, Ken said:

"This is astonishing. A Cheat. How did you find out we're here?"

"My brother told me she can't be trusted, she comes to the beach to meet men who are loaded with dosh. If I had told you the first time I saw you two together, you would have known, to avoided being taken in by her."

"Thanks for letting me know. Damn it, I was fond of the girl. Excuse me awhile Bob, I want to go on a walk and think awhile."

Ken went out on the pier and looked down on the incoming waves and pondered to himself. It was too much for him to take in, he decided to go back and mingled with the crowd on the mall and tried to forget Rosie.

Ken then felt the most gentle, passionate, arms wrapped around his waist-line. Glancing around, he saw the smiling face of the most beautiful girl in the world.

"Oh my gosh! Lucy," Ken said. "At last you're here!"

"I just bump into an acquaintance, that runs the cocktail shack, he told me you were down here.

Ken spent the evening with Lucy. One night a few days later, he proposed to her on the pier.

"A big yes, my handsome knight" Lucy replied, "if you can give me your word of honor that you've never been in love with any one else."

"That's easily given. You're the only girl I've ever loved."

And they live happily ever after.

From this short story it is easy to say that;-

Love is the most metallic of emotions. It will build about its phenomenon a temple of adoration, it will give all, yet brutally clinch everything; it delights in pleasing, yet it sometimes purposefully wounds; its divine tenderness often combine into an asperity, extraordinary symbol of universal duality, it is at once brutish and angelic.

Nothing stands still in this planet earth, not even love: it must grow or it fades. Perhaps, that is the strongest love which conquers the peerless number of hindrance. Love to some is a poison; to others an affliction. To us all it is an obligation. As is one's honor, so is one's love. Perhaps the deepest love is the most reserved.

If you have two emotional human souls, the one loves passionately and the other not at all, the other is unconsciously blind to love's outcry and claims, the one may affectionately urge; the other passively surrenders.

Of a great and respond in kind love, there is one and only one sign: the expression of the eyes. Who that has seen it was ever cheated by its copy. Did ever the same love light shine in that same eyes twice?

The light of love in the eyes may take on hundreds of forms: ecstatic joy, a trustful happiness; infinite alleviation's, maybe numerous promises untold, a devotion supreme, or even a complex gift, tenderness indescribable, implicit believe, unquestioning tenacity, bountiful compassion, cheeky desires. He who shall count the stars of paradise, shall recite the glares of love.

To each of us we are the central part of the visible universe. But when love comes it modifies this geocentric universe. Yet, it is a important fact that love, which, more than any other thing in this world, is the champion bearer of our hearts, begins its magical work as a divider. For when love first lights in the chest of the young, it throws about its phenomenon a sacred radiance, which amazes at the same time that it inspires the loyal fan.

Can only two people walk side by side in the path of love? Love raises everything to a higher plane; but nothing superior than the man or woman who is loved. Is there anything about which love does not shed a aura?

True love makes all things delightful, except perhaps the companion. Was there ever man or woman yet who was not bettered by a true love? True love is ever bashful and jittery of its own daring. But this not every human being understandings.

Too often the fantasy of love and not the truth wins the day. Humans who seek a real lover should beware the overconfident one.

They are happiest who can longest disbelieve in the futility of this apprentice blend; for it may be that such wonder is favorable to romance.

Love is not explicitly an offering, it is an exchange. The lover, indeed, gives his heart; he expects another in return.

Love is like life; no mechanism can produce it, and nothing in the promise land above or on earth, beneath or in the waters under the earth will restore it.

How many a desperate human wight has tried to resurrect love!

To such heights does love exalt the lover that he or she will live for days in the remembered delights of a look, a word, a gesture.

Thee is one thing which is impossible to love. Love cannot devise love; the extreme and most heartfelt love is powerless to conjure a sparkle of love.

Hate may be hidden, love never. The more the extravagant apex of love, the lower the fiery point. But love cannot always be kept at pinnacle compression.

A young person think love is the winning-post of life, the older know it's a turn in the course. Although, it is a crucial turn. In love, the imagery plays a very huge part. And this may be variously described. Human's view love as a sort of sacred belief.

Love knows no ideology. Love acknowledges no idol but itself and accepts no commands but its own, it is free. There are two codes of ethics, one that of the romantic heart; the other that of the practical head.

There are as many ways of making love as there are of cooking meat. And maybe there are as many kinds of love as there are of seasonings or spices.

Love speaks three languages: one with the lips; the tongue, the other with the eyes. Lovers always talk in a mysterious tongue. Most times certain eyes and lips will charm, while others leave us frosty and motionless? Is the force in the eyes, on the tongue, and the lips, or is there some enigmatic and psychic power?

To try and win and keep another heart, is something wee should try and find out for our self. All we know is that there is nothing more dynamic than passion.

In the animosity of the composition of love, love laughs at promises.

The onset of love is as when one starts a fire. The eye tells more than the sweet words from a tongue. And, if the eye and the tongue disprove each other, believe the eye.

Whatsoever gives intense joy is the conjuration of underlying passion. For each person takes pleasure in believing that him or her only can elicit this passion.

Making love is a sort of combat, the conditions of which are that the man shall feel like a mighty and victorious and the woman goes in a world of ecstasy.

The battle of love-making can be an unequal combat, even were both male and female are fully blazed; For each man she meets, a woman carries in her glimmer a beam. If that misses its aim, she is powerless: it is like a arrow without a bow; when fired, the man can close.

The heroic of love is not only by chance but one of skill. What so ever annoys man is that a woman bluff, that she must be outwit by tricks. However, the coldest woman sometimes thaws

With women, nothing is more conquering than conquest; nothing so invincible as battles of love. A man cherish what he has fought for. No one knows this better than a woman. Protection on the part of a woman is a wall which a man is predicted to leap. His sprightliness is the measure of her approval.

If a man arouse a woman's passion, he arouse a lot. However, if he failed, then it's best for him to depart.

When a man thinks he can at any time excerpt himself from any female complexity that he may choose to have disentangled, he's a dunce.

Cheerful expressions touches our hearts

Who doesn't enjoy looking upon the beautiful lady, with a bright, cheerful face, laughing eyes, well shaped curvy body, and all that? Every man! That's right especially me. And when the grumpy lady of heartaches scamper close by you, how do you feel? Just about as cheery as if she'd come to ask you to attend a sending off! One of the first things we should try to remember in the development of beauty is expression.

My dear ladies, made up of sugar, spices, and all other things which nice, it doesn't matter if you have a few freckles, or if your nose bends or crooked up just a little too much, if your lips are large or small, if you have a jolly, golden face people will always call you beautiful. You can count on that always. Marvelous essence is a admirable beautifier. It sparkles the eyes, hinders impending wrinkles, and brings the cosmos blossom tints into your cheeks.

The kind of beauty that attracts me is the sort that is active, doing, achieving, and working for something marvelous. I completely believe, that we can all look at our best and still not look as if we were made of curtail mirror

I often stare at things around me and think of what a enormous deal of work there is in this great, huge, beautiful world. To me, the idle woman is not a beautiful woman. She is like the lady in the picture frame looking impractical that hangs in the passageway. But the other woman, the gorgeous and the useful lady oh man! she is a sight for sore eyes, and to make old eyes grow young. Her clothing is clean, no matter if it's expensive or not, her hair all washed, brush and lovely, her teeth is clean. She glides and some steps along quickly, and you know then, by the very air about her that she is a worker, regardless if she's of the smart set or of the factory minimum wage worker that toils and toils from dusk till dawn.

During the night in the face and hands can be well washed, and creamed, the hair brushed and combed, the teeth well cleaned and the mouth washed. And of course, your partner or lover can cream your beautiful legs with particular care.

A woman's face, being the most sensitive, is usually the first part of the body to be doleful. The therapy for facial blemishes is found in exercise, baths and a circumspect diet. Not too much facial night cream.

A shape of stress will at times bring a heart-mangle batch of flare-up to the surface of the skin, and this condition is best treated by plenty of baths, lots of fresh air, exercise, and a cheerful courage to bolster up and not have any hysteria which, by the way, is easier said than putting into action, as most of us know our own unhappiness.

There's a commodity about a woman's hair that sparkle most men hearts with lust, the beauty and styling of a woman's hair regardless it be long, short, shoulder length, straight, curly, blondes, brunettes, auburn, and hybrid does cheers a man. His face displays vibrant expression.

I'd like to share a brief story about a girl who's hair radiates cheer, joy and happiness.

Some many years ago there was a girl by the name of Ellie who had very long and very beautiful hair. Her brothers, who were as well spoken and protective as most brothers usually are, were in the mode of saying that she was a perfect carrot. Her hair was very much the color of a hazel, and she took the best possible care of it. It was a power of life with her, when she had nothing else to do, she would brush her hair. Time and time again she brushed it when she had other things to do. She never have it cut. She even refused a plats or locks of it from anyone. When she went out for walks with her brother,s she listened mindfully as people passed her, Most of the times, they said things about her hair which she liked very much. Then she would try not to look delighted, and when a girl who is really charm tries to look as if she did not care, she looks perfectly disgusting. Her brothers often comment on it.

Her mother, who was a exceptional and wise lady, described to her how cruel pride was, notably pride about people's hair. She express to her that special attractions, peculiarly if associated in any way with the hair, were insignificant as contrast with the thoughtful and noble trait. On the other hand, her mother took her to a photographer and had her taken photos in various positions, and they all made such beautiful pictures that the photographer almost use swear words because she was not sanction to display them on her website.

When she reached her late teens, most of her girl friends had a girl wishes to have long dresses and do their hair up into curly waves, but this girl would not have her hair in curly waves, and was rude to the principal of the school. In the climax, of course, Ellie had to surrendered, for it is not custom for girls of a certain age to wear their hair down they way Ellie did at the school. But she became immensely creative. She had ways of doing her hair so that it would not look wavy, but plummet down surprisingly and caused exceptional fondness. She would then profess to be baffled and awkward. Now, when a girl who is not in the least bemused and flustered tries to look so, she looks simply witless. Her brothers told her so. Every single friend she had, and many who were only acquaintances, had seen Ellie's hair in its home-grown glory. Some of her friends raved about it to Ellie's brothers, and were surprised that the brothers did not share their ardor.

"Ellie has such a lot of it," her friends would say.

"She thinks a lot of it," her brothers would answer.

Now, Ellie and her female friends were not the only girls in the world, and they could not know all the rest; thus a girl called Kym came to them as something of a notion. As she was called Kym, she was, of course, quite good. Kym is lovely girls name. If you ask anyone if Kym is clever, they reply that she is a good cleaner. If you ask if she is stunning, people would change the topic of looking attractive quickly. There was nothing ravishing about this Kym. She was just Kym.

It is a very true that it is the people who are naturally the loveliest to look at who take the most time to look pretty. The woman who, so far as her face is uptight makes the best of a bad job, is rare. Kym was not a stunner, but she was astute and intelligent. She would normally dressed herself quickly in things that sport well. She would brag that she could do her hair without a mirror, and everyone who saw her hair believed it. But as it happened, when Kym met Ellie, a change came over her.

"Your hair is perfectly angelic," she said to Ellie.

Ellie tried to be respectfully apathy.

"So kind of you to say so," she said.

"And you do it so beautifully," said Kym. "I'm longing for some design for my hair, so that it wouldn't look appalling."

"It isn't dire at all," said Ellie, kindly. "I don't think there's any changes to be made if I were you."

Then she went into depict and showed Kym that the thing was grim and that reform was impossible. Of course, she did not use those words, and was warmly graceful about it.

Now, that same night, as Ellie was having her own hair brushed, a dreadful feeling came over her. She put it aside as a thing flawlessly ludicrous. It might have been a ploy of the mirror. It might have been her own fantasy. It did not keep her awake for a short time. However, the next morning one of her brothers came into her room, looked at her, and said:

"What a dimwit you were to have your hair cut!"

"I have not had it cut," said Ellie, frenziedly. "It's the same length."

"Nonsense," said the brother. "It's much shorter."

"It's not," said Ellie; " leave me alone. I can't get on properly while you're hanging around."

The brother went away, and Ellie dash to the mirror. The warm morning sunshine verified her notions of the night before. Her brother was surely right. Ellie's hair was much shorter.

At midday Ellie secretly went to one of the best hair stylist. She had seen the advert, and she felt that here the stylist might at any cost know the worst.

As each day passes her hair seemed to be a bit shorter. This was notably the case when she had been behaving like a spiteful cub. It reached a point when all her friends who met her bellowed. "Why, Ellie, what on earth have you done to your hair?"

Then she would smile sweetly and say: "Brushed it as usual" But inwardly she was a sad girl.

To escape the sweet empathy of her friends and family she went away to reside in a little cottage with her grandfather near a forest. It is good for a girl who has been seeing so many people to stay by herself for a little while. It was also good for a girl who has been long in a crowded city to go away into the country side remoteness. Your soul must go to the cleaner, just like your clothing.

Now that there was no one to take pity with her hair loss, and no one to attract by her lovely hair even if she had still had it long, she started to ponder on other things. And she thought about rabbits, and berries, beautiful sunsets,swans swimming in ponds, and streams that made shiny lines down the hillsides. Each morning she went all by herself to a stream half a mile from her grandfather cottage by herself.

The meet an old man who was tall, slim, and always polite, to feed the fishes bread crumbs, but also he had very sad looking face. He had the face of one who never fail to ache. After Ellie had been three weeks in her grandfather cottage she suddenly saw that this old, slim, man had always looked really forsaken. The sadness of other people had never made a difference to Ellie before; but now one morning she asked the old man why this was, and if there were anything that she could do for him.

The slim old man said

"I have a daughter and she was once very pretty. Everyone that saw her never forgot how beautiful she was. And she fell sick of a bizarre sickness so that part of her face became detestable. I'm the only one who can bear to look at her face, unless their dreams should be spooky for ever."

"Does she lives here, with you. your daughter?" asked Ellie.

"Yes; she lies in the room all day."

"I will come up and see to her," said Ellie, "and help nurse her, for you must often be away on your errands."

"No," said the frail looking old man, "that is too much for you to do. I tell you that no one but myself can bear to look at her."

"Look at me," said Ellie. As she took off the big hat that she always wore to cover her head. "I had beautiful long hair once," Ellie said, "and I have lost most of. Please let me try and help you."

Then Ellie went back to the old man house. She entered a room which was darkened, and even in that faint light she could see the old man's daughter, who was once very pretty, and now became painful to see. Ellie was a bit fearful, but tried not to reveal it, and a girl who is spooked and tries not to show it, very usually does not look nearly such a dimwit as she thinks. Ellie stayed there a long time, and when she came out her face was quite pale, and she wanted to go back to her grandfather cottage and weep.

But each morning after that until the last week came, she went to see the sick girl who loved and cherish her. Sadly the end came one morning very quietly. And the old frail man did not cry at that time, but he blessed Ellie. Next morning when Ellie rise it was a bit later than see would normally do, and the lovely late morning sun was gushing through her room window. For a while she meditated with her eyes tightly closed, figuring out all that had happened. Each visit to the sick girl had been a something special and meaningful to her, but now she grieved that the girl was now deceased, and wondered in her mind if there were none other for whom she might find to talk to apart from her beloved grandpa.

At last, since it was no use to lie in so late, she sprang up on her feet, and, alas, loads of beautiful hazel-coloured hair fell far down over her slender shoulders! She washed her face and open her eyes in astonishment. and thought hat she must be dreaming. However, it had really happened. Her mirror revealed the truth. The grandeur of her beautiful hair had come back as strangely as it had gone. So that day she mused what she would do as, she spotted some lovely flowers next to her grandfather cottage, she made a necklace of flowers. Ones that you would normally see people wearing in Hawaii.

She went to see the old frail man. And thank him for his blessings. For once the old man heart was fill with happiness and a cheerful smile on his thin face. She returned to her grandfather cottage with a very cheerful heart. Her grandfather was tickled with laughter, to see his grand daughter happy again.

The following day she hugged her grandad goodbye, and went back to her own home; and her brothers were all joyful to see her, and cherish the sight her beautiful hair, and were very happy that it had grown again so quickly.

Ellie was never boastful and grisly again; she was very nice, so that the handsome who married her, loved her as much for the sweetness of her heart as for her angel's face and her beautiful long hair.

Cheerful Music

Music is the mirror which most splendidly reflects human's inner soul and the element of all things. The spiritual share of music intrigues to the spiritual hearts of human's, conveying each heart akin to the cravings and magnitudes of each. The material share of music may be correlate to the body in which man's spirit is bestowed. It is the channel which carries messages of music from soul to soul through the medium of the human ear.

The impulse to demonstrate feeling by means of sound is universally acknowledge, and sound, carried with feelings, are peculiarly exciting to human beings. The dancing of people may be increased by the emotional tones of its leading movers.

We really try honestly, to show off our dance moves and swung our ladies, although many were good dancers to get round. Once were not invited to a ball; the dance becomes on of cheer delight.

Short story on music

They dance and dined with. Happiness, pleasure, joy, smiles, at least. and while Jamie stood thinking of herbal tea, when the house began to surge with young people who had dined upstairs or downstairs, on they way to Jamie's, or not at all, only heaven's knows elsewhere. The hall room doors were thrown open again, the floor was cleared as if by magic, partners caught hold of each other, a group ganged up in the middle of the hall room, and one, two, one-two-three, they were in the middle of a showing of their dancing credentials to Prince and the Revolution; Wonderful song: Raspberry Beret. Before Jamie could recover any pleasantry.

They kept on bouncing around in delight like happy children in a story book again and again, when Jamie received a finger jab in the region of the stomach. It was is cousin himself, who shouted:

"Come on man; on the dance floor you go, and move your legs. Don't stand there like the statue of liberty, now show what kind of fellow you are with those long legs of yours, that our creation has sent you out upon."

Jamie started dancing; although he did not at all like is cousin's way of putting him on the spot. Jamie almost stole the lime light from the rest of the dancers. Songs after songs Jamie had a dance move for each music the DJ selected.

Jamie's cousin even became lively; and everything might have blew off in joy and happiness if his cousin had not taken it into his head that he wasn't doing any justice on the dance floor, especially when he was waltzing with a beautiful lady.

"What kind of dancing is that to show to people?' Jamie asked his cousin insultingly. "There you go, tripping all over like some kind of domino effect."

Jamie's cousin ignored him. Each time that Jamie's cousin passed the dance room floor, his dancing skills look somewhat like a beginner clueless to dancing. The only good performance he did, was when the DJ started playing slow jam.

But what was the use? Each time the cousin came back from his round through the non-smoking-room, where he cooled his head with the light of a huge spliff, he felt heroic and more, heroic, until at last he decided to chill for a bit with some cool beer. When he got all excited and started dancing, and singing. Perhaps I should say screaming his voice was like the roar of some hungry lion.

"Out of the way with these crazy dancing" he cried. "Now, let me showing some real popular dance. Come, sweetie-pie, we two old ones will make these silly youngsters a thing or two"

"Oh, no, I'm not a good dancer," she responded respectable

"Only Beelzebub is old," Jamie cousin laugh merrily; "your smile, charisma, and charm, with your bouncy hair will make us look like magnificent dancers under the flashy, colorful disco lights. So come along, pretty woman!'

"Please, I'm a rubbish dancer, no, my dear I don't want to make a fool of myself; won't you excuse me?' pleaded the pretty lady. A few ladies volunteered to dance with Jamie's cousin. But it was no use. A part of the hall was cleared, room had to be made, people were were squeezing up against the walls, so they could be out of the way, at all events.

Some of the young ladies were galled at the interruption, and some gentlemen were more or less sulky over all the dispersing crowd that they had felt.

The gorgeous lady who had to dance was quite in fear if the crowd who laughed at her dancing skills. She started to dance with, Jamie's cousin, who would only stare politely at her over his spectacles, and kept going with another old fashion kind of dance.

As far as Jamie's cousin was concerned, every member of his family are good enough for any or every dance; and as to the dance itself, the beat of music was really important; for, you see it happened in this way:

Jamie's cousin came swinging in with one arm by his side, and swirl round and round like a spinning wheel, respectable the beautiful lady on the other arm. He placed her with a courtly sweep in the middle of the floor, bowed in the fashion of the applauding crowd, with head down between his legs and arms hanging in front, but quickly straightened himself up again and looked about with a cheeky smile.

Jamie's cousin, now with his shirt unbuttoned, rocking away to the song: If you think I'm sexy. Was a sight to see in the dance-room. Though is was middle aged is movements were very agile

Jamie himself was shock, the crowd kept cheering his cousin on. He took shirt off, and instead of dancing he was mainly showing off is big muscles. A few young pretty girls when close up to him. Some where taking photos of him. The others where recording him on their mobile phones.

Jamie's cousin waved his hands towards the DJ requesting 80s disco songs.

"Now, watch me, you shall see a dance worth looking at!" And then he started dancing again.

The DJ struck up some really good 80s disco tunes. Jamie's uncle showed off all the 80s disco dance moves.

All attention was now concentrated upon Jamie's cousins legs; it was clear that after so much dancing, he started tiring.

Jamie stood and wondered whether his cousin would spring into the air clear over the crowd who circled him. or only kick fall into the crowd.

That would have been quite like him, and it is not at all certain whether he himself did not think of dancing for so long.

After some little tired dancing, he somehow saved some of his energies for the decisive action, he powerfully stamped his feet upon the floor.

As if he had trodden upon soft leaves, in a flash his heels glided forward from under him. He fell backward upon his bum with heavy thud sound, his legs beat the air, and the crown of his head struck a man with a boom that resounded through the dance floor.

Yes, there he was, he lay stretched in all his wonder, with his back just in front of the feet of a respectable gentleman, who resembled a deserted pillar in the wild.

A group of young girls creased themselves into cheerful laughter.

Jamie was profane enough to let a few men picked him up. Of course his cousin would not fall to pieces.

 Jamie slipped out into the beer garden and laughed until he was quite exhausted.

Since then Jamie's cousin have often speculate what kind of dance it could have been.

A cheerful smile

Robert bowed with a shy clunk expressing himself as if to say, there's a fair bet he needed cheering somewhere and presented Amy with a perfect cocktail on a shine silver tray. Robert stood holding the tray, with a permanent enamel smile on his smooth face, as Amy savor the cocktail through a slim straw and smirk.

"It's a tasty cocktail, Robert," said Amy. "Cheers. But, dammit, I wish you didn't have that everlasting smile!"

"I am very sorry, Miss Amy, but I am unable to adjust myself in any way," replied Robert in his polite, deep voice.

He excused himself to a corner and stood placidly, still holding the tray. Robert had found a silver deposit and made the tray.

"Sometimes," one of Robert friends said nostalgically, "it seems to me it would be better to live in a forest shack with a real man than in a mansion with Robert."

The three women sprawled comfortably in the sitting room of their massive house, as luxurious as anything any of them would have known on Earth. The floor and pine flooring, the furniture was expensively made from mahogany wood, the art work on the walls were very artistic and uplifting, the shelves were filled with gossip magazines.

Robert had done it all, made furniture, and some of the most exquisite art work which any millionaire would be more than happy to purchase.

"Do you suppose we'll ever escape from this best of all possible virility worlds?" asked Paula, running her fingers through her thick blonde curly hair with her fingers and inspecting herself in front of a mirror.

"I don't see how," answered mousey brown hair Amy unpleasantly. "That barometrically bait crash any other car just as it damage ours, and the same magnetic layer prevents any frequency messages from coming out. So, I'm afraid we're a outpost."

"An outpost sustains itself," said straight-faced Laura, sharply. "We aren't a population, without men."

They were not the most stunning three young women in the universe. However they were young enough, rice enough, and healthy enough, to attract most men.

It had been a short six months now revolving around these three ladies. Robert, was like their little robot, he was compliant and skillful and had provided them with furniture and other material things.

Robert could not create a man. Robert did could not introduce them to any male friends, the few he had were married. He had tried once to introduce male acquaintances, when he had overheard them wishing for one.

"It's been a hot day," said Amy, fanning her face. "I wish the temperature would cool down a bit."

Silently, Robert moved from the sitting room and went outside.

Karl nodded after him with a nasty little laugh.

"It'll rain this evening," she said.

The air condition in the house was a bit faulty. Amy asked, Robert who had not quite completed the task of air-conditioning the house.

An accident just happened, someone got knock over by a speeding car , who did not stop to check the victim.

 The person was unconscious, but alive. And he was a man!

They all carried him back to the house, affectionately, and put him to bed. They hovered over him like three hens over a single chick, waiting and watching for him to come out of his coma, while Robert scampered about and administering the necessary first aid treatments.

"He'll live," said a nurse. Who arrived shortly after the incident "He'll be on his feet and walking around in a couple weeks."

"A man!" Paula said softly, with something like admiration in her voice.

"I believe our little friend Robert powers brought him here in answer to our prayers."

"Now, ladies," said Amy, "we have to realize that a man can brings problems, as well as happiness."

There was a rigidity to her tone which almost hide the tremor behind it. There was a defiant note of competition there which had not been seen for quite sometime.

"What do you mean?" Laura.

"I understand what Amy means," said Laura, and the new grimness came natural to her.

"She means, which one of us gets him?"

Paula, the eldest, gulped, and her mouth rounded with a little smile. Karl blinked, as though she were coming out of a startle.

"That's right," said Amy. "When he gets well can we draw three bits, or do we let him choose?"

"Can't we wait for him to get well?" propose Paula shyly.

Robert came in the room with a new thermometer and poked it into the unconscious man's mouth. He stood by the bed, waiting bravely.

"No, I don't think we should wait," said Amy. "I think we are obliged to have it all agreed on, so there won't be any controversy about it."

"Let us draw straws," said Laura. Laura's face was straight, and she had a slim figure.

Paula, the eldest, opened her mouth, but Karl stole a march on her.

"We don't have to follow olden days philosophies, and we shouldn't. There's only one solution that will keep everyone happy, all of us and the man." She said strongly

"That's it?" asked Karl torridly.

"Polygamy, of course. He may belong to us all."

Paula shivered but, shockingly, she shook her head slowly.

"That's sounds great," agreed Laura, "but we should agree that any of us will be favored than the others. He needs to comprehend that from the start."

"That sound fair," said Amy, biting her lips. "Yes, that's good. However, I agree with Laura. He should quality and equally times among us."

Jabbering over the attribute, the arduous vying disappeared from their tones, the three left the sickroom to prepare dinner.

After the meal they went back in.

Robert stood by the bed, the eternal smile of service on his young baby face. Cheered the three ladies.

Cheerful laughter

Long, long ago there was a hilarious old man who liked to laugh and to make cup cakes from from all variety of ingredient.

One day, while he was baking some cup cakes for supper, one fell, and it rolled under a table in the kitchen floor of his little kitchen and vanish. The old man tried to reach it by putting his hand down a hole, that was by a corner of his kitchen floor.

The old man sight wasn't great so, after having looked and feel for this cupcake in vain, he thought that it must have rolled deeper away down the hole. He ran out of the kitchen and down the road, shouting: "My cup cake! my cup cake! Where is that cup cake of mine?"

After a short while he saw a signage standing by the roadside, and he said, calling it by its name:

"O John did you see my cup cake?"

John replied:

"Yes, I saw your cup cake spinning pass me down the road. However, I shall warn there's a haunted man living down the bottom of this road, if I were you I'd turn back."

But the old man laughed, and ran on farther down the road, shouting: "My cup cake! my cup cake! Where is that cup cake of mine?" And she came to another statue of another John, and asked it:

"O kind John, did you see my cup cake?"

And John said:

"Yes, I saw your cup cake go by a short while ago. But you must not go any farther, because there is a haunted man down there who scares the living daylight out of people."

The old man laughed and ran on, still shouting out: "My cup cake! my cup cake! Where is that cup cake of mine?" And he came to a third John, and asked it:

"O dear John, did you see my cup cake?"

However, John said:

"Don't talk about your cup cake now. Here is the haunted man coming.Hide down here behind me, and be extremely quite."

The haunted man came very close, and stopped and bowed to John, and said:

"Good day, John!"

John said good day, too, with a very pleasant reply.

Then the old haunted man suddenly sniffed the air a few times in a suspicious way, and shouted out: "John, John! I smell the smell of mankind somewhere don't you?"

"No!" said John, "I believe you are mistaken."

"No, no!" said the haunted man after sniffing the air again; "I smell the smell of mankind."

Then the old man hidden behind John could not help laughing"He-he-he-he!"and the haunted man instantly reached down his large sweaty hand behind John's sleeve, and pulled the old baker out, still laughing, "He-he-he-he!"

"Ah! ha!" cried the haunted man

Then John said:

"What are you going to do with that good old man? Please don't hurt him."

"I won't," said the haunted man "but I will take him home with me to bake for us."

"He-he-he-he!" laughed the old man.

"Very well," said John, "but you must really be kind to him. If you are not, I will be very angry."

"I won't hurt him all," promised the haunted man; "and he will only have to do a little work for us each day. Good-by, John."

Then the haunted man took the old man far down the road until they came to a stream, where there was a wooden bridge, He put the baker old man on his back, and took him across the stream to his house. It was a old haunted house. He led him at once into the kitchen, and told him to bake some buns for supper. And he gave him a small wooden spoon, and said:

"Bake old man bake. Bake old man bake until. The oven his filled with baked buns"

So the old man did as the haunted man told him, and began to bake within an hour the oven was filled with buns.

After that, the humorous old man stayed a long time in the house of the haunted man, and every day baked cakes for him and for all his friends. The haunted never hurt or frightened him, and he work was made quite easy by a magic wooden spoon, although she had to bake a very, large amount of cakes.

But he felt lonely, and always wanted very much to go back to his own little house, and make his cup cakes; and one day, when the haunted man were all out somewhere, he thought he would try to run away.

He first took the magic wooden spoon and slipped it under his arm in a bag and then he went down to the stream. No one saw him.cross over on the wooden bridge to the other side.

The haunted man came back to the haunted house with his friends.

They found that their baker was gone, and the magic wooden spoon as well. They ran down to the stream at once, and saw the old man far away.

The haunted man had magical powers. So him and his friends knelt down on their needs and spoke in mysterious tongues.

It somehow happened that through the magical words the haunted man and his friends said, helped them closing in on the old baker man.

Then the old baker man for the first time in his life got very serious and he dropped the bag that had the magical wooden spoon, took the magic wooden spoon from out of the bag, and shook it at the haunted man and made such funny faces that the haunted man and his friends all burst out With non-stop laughter.

They kept laughing and laughing, until the moment came when the haunted old man and his friends fell into the stream, they could not swim. They laughed until they all drowned.

The comical old man ran away up the road as fast as he could. He didn't stopped to say hello to any of the John's. He kept running until he found himself at home again, still feeling and looking serious.

The next day he was happy again, for he could make cup cakes whenever he liked. The bonus, he had the magic wooden spoon to bake extra cakes faster. He started selling his cup cakes to the locals living in the community, and after a while he became prosperous and happily ever after.

Short tale of laughter

Long time a go a vexed man laid some corn in a bowl, intending to put it in the soup he was going to cook. But a pet bird that a man, his neighbor, had ate it up. Seeing this, the vexed face man seized the pet bird and, said. "You despicable thing!" cut its beak and let it go.

When the man who lived next door heard that his pet bird had got its beak cut for its misdeed, he was greatly bemoaning, and set out with his wife over hills and fields to find where it had gone, weeping: "Where is my pet bird staying? Where does my pet bird stay?"

Eventually they found its home. When the pet bird saw that its master and mistress had come to find it, the pet bird reveled with joy, and brought them next to its hut and appreciated them for their kindness in past times.

It danced a hop called the small bird dance, and thus they spent the day. When it got dark, and there was talk of going home, the pet bird brought out two tape up boxes and said.

"Will you take the large one, or shall I give you the small one?" The man and his wife replied.

"We are old, so give us the small one, it will be easier to carry it."

The pet bird then gave them the small box, and they returned with it to their home.

"Lets open and see what is in it," the man said to his beloved wife.

They opened the box and looked in it, they found gold coins. They never expected or seen so many gold coins.The more coins they took out, the more they found inside. The supply was enormous, so that their home at once became wealthy and prosperous.

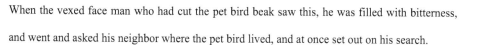

When the vexed face man who had cut the pet bird beak saw this, he was filled with bitterness, and went and asked his neighbor where the pet bird lived, and at once set out on his search.

Once a gain the pet bird brought out two taped up boxes, and asked like before.

"Will you take the large box, or shall I give you the small box?"

Thinking the gold coins would be large in quantity to the weight of the tape box, the vexed faced man replied.

"Let me have the large one."

Receiving the large box. The vexed faced man started home with it on his back, the small pet bird laughing at him as he went. It was as heavy as lead, and difficult to carry, but at last he got back with it to his home.

Then, when the vexed face man took off the tape, open the box and looked in, a whole swarm of fly came popping out from the inside of the box, and at once they caught her up and feast on the vexed face man.

Short tale of laughter

A lady who was considered the most meticulous of all the residents in a palace heard of another woman who was the most careful on planet earth. She said to her daughter.

"We, live on little, but if we were more careful still, we might live on nothing at all. It will be well noble for us to get guidance in savings from the careful woman."

The daughter agreed, and both decided that the daughter should go and probe whether the genius in profit-making science would take pupils. A barter of presents being a necessary preparatory to closer dealings, the woman told the daughter to take two coins, and to buy a cheap bread from the grocery store. The daughter, by way of thinking, got two loaves of bread. The mother put away bread. She put in a colorful carry bag, as if it were the thing which it represented, the usual gift sent in symbol of great respect. The daughter took the carry bag, and after a short journey reached the house of the most careful man on this earth.

The chief of the house was absent, but her daughter received the traveler, listened to her reasons for visiting the home, and accepted the gifts. Having taken from the carry bag the loaf of bread she said kindly to her visitor.

"I am sorry that we have nothing in this house that is deserving to take the place of this loaf of bread in your carry bag. I will, however, declare our friendly encounter of it by giving you six carrots for you to take home with you."

The daughter of the most careful woman in the domain then took the carry bag and went to her mother to tell of parsimony exceeding her own.

When the most careful woman in the on earth returned home, her daughter told her that a visitor had been there, having come from a short distance to take lessons in profit-making. The mother asked what gift was brought as an influx, and the daughter showed the loaf of bread on the kitchen table. The mother looked at it, and then asked her daughter what she had barter as a return gift. The daughter told her, she gave the visitor six large carrots and placed them in the visitor's carry bag. The mother instantly flew into a horrible fury and use her middle finger and knock it on the girl forehead saying.

"You costly brute! Why did you give the visitor six large carrots, instead of two small ones?"

Short smiling letters

We do not begin to say

A cheerful, support is always given

That helps us to rise above earthly things

Just like birds fly high with precious wings.

Our life's has taught us each day

cherish each moment as long as we live

Life sometime seems like a darkness of gloom,

Yet, don't forget the world is a tomb that

sweet flowering spring up from the dust.

Balm is sent to ease our pain,

There's no need to quarrel or explain

Gratitude educates the heart and soul.

It expresses an elevating art

It gives our aching minds an inner sight

and surely brings it near the fathomless.

Love lift us up, even when nothing else will help.

Even when you do find love,

It is wise and kind not to be blind to it,

There's no need to look for the virtue behind love;

For ever cloudy night has a hint of light

The current of life keeps running away

But deep down inside of us we know it's time for love

Never think to alter love's motion.

Don't ever waste a curse on the universe,

It came here before us

The universe will never adjust itself to suit us

Some things must go wrong in your life

And the sooner you know it, the better, that a wonderful smile cheers us all

Cheerful Friendship

The language of true friendship is not words, but actions with meanings. It is an intelligence above any language. A true friendship is as wise as it is kind-hearted. The parties to it yield completely to the direction of their love, and know no other law or goodwill. It is not costly and deranged, but what it says is something established from now on, and will bear to be fashioned. It is a truer truth, it is better and honourable news, and no time will ever be shame, or prove it to be untrue. This is a flower which thrives best in a pleasant zone, where spring and summer oscillate with each other. The friend is an essential, and meets his or her friend on homely ground; not in bars and cushions, but on the ground, and on sea rocks they will sit, abiding the natural and primitive laws. They will meet without any howl, and part without loud regrets. Their relation signifies such qualities as the warrior accolades.

Friendship does not stand for numbers; A true friend does not count his friends on his fingers; they are not numerable. The more there are included by this affiliation, if they are indeed included, the fewer and diviner the quality of the love that holds them together. We cannot have too many associates; the ethics that we cherish, we to some extent connect, so that we are made at last more suitable for most relation of life.

There's a danger in friendship, it will end. It is a delicate flower. The smallest unsuitable, even if it be unknown to one's self, depraves it. Let the friend know that those faults that they detect in their friend, their own faults attract. There is no rule more immovable than that we are paid for our cynicism by finding what we think. By our pettiness and prejudices we say, I'll have so much and such of you, my friend. Perhaps there are none gracious, none impartial, none wise, and heroic enough for a true and lasting friendship.

My Friend is not of some other country or family, but cells of my cells. He is my real brother and sister. I see the friend yonder even thou we live far apart.

Life has no pleasure towering or aristocratic than that of friendship. It is awful to consider that this glorious enjoyment may end by countless causes, and that there is no human assets of which the extent is less certain.

Many have talked, in very lofty languages, of the endurance of friendship, of unbeatable steadfastness, and deep-rooted kindness. In life we've have seen men who have continued loyal to their earliest choice, and whose closeness has dominate over changes of fortune, and contrast of assumption.

A man dispossess of the colleague to whom he used to open his chest, and with whom he shared the hours of relaxation and enjoyment, feels the day at first hanging heavy upon him; his challenges overwhelm, and his doubts bewilders him. He sees time come and go without his custom gratification, and all its sadness within him. However, this uneasiness never long live. essentials produces opportune, new laughter are uncovered and new conversation are disclosed.

Friendship is often destroyed by resistance of passion, not only by the clumsy and visible concerns which the desire of riches and strength forms and continues, but by loads of secrets seldom known to the mind upon which they work. There is hardly anyone without some favourite dabble that they values above greater reaping, some may desire minor praise which they cannot bravely suffer to be resented.

This, however, is a unhurried malice, which a wise person will preclude as contrary with silence, and a good person will repress as discordant to virtue. However, human happiness is sometimes infringed by some more rapid blows.

A key fruit of friendship is the ease and release of the swellings of the heart, which passions of all kinds do origin and convince. There's no reception that opens the heart, but a loving true friend; to whom you may disclose griefs, joys, fears, hopes, suspicions, caution, and whatsoever rest upon the heart, to afflict it, in a kind of acknowledgement.

Letters to Fanny

Tony friend Cheryl never fails to delight and confound Lynn. Much as she gives, there is in her boundlessly more to get. Lynn relation with her never goes on, and it never goes back. It leads nowhere. Cheryl and Lynn stop together in the midst of their plight and look about them. And what they see in the mirror about is all and enough to consider.

O you think, Cheryl" Lynn said to her on a day that she felt really low, "that most things maybe really related?"
The face of Cheryl was calm, and also the ocean.

"Relative!" said Cheryl. "Nothing is relative. I tell you nothing is relative. I am from the Fiji. In Fiji, when I was very young to everything, there was an grisly bug-eyed woman who bathed me and creamed my skin, and dressed me in beautiful dresses. Also the bug-eyed woman looked into my discomfort young eyes with her grisly bug-eyes so that my tiny young soul was nudged as any pins. The bug-eyed woman did these things to upset me, she disliked me for being one of the most beautiful girl in Fiji. She was a horrid, grisly brute."

"That was not relative. I tell you now, that was not relative," said Cheryl.

"If I had been an troublesome, overgrown person and that bug-eyed woman had pinched my little arms still she would have been a horrid, grisly brute."

"If I had been a ruthless spirit and that bug-eyed woman had looked into my savage eyes with her grisly bug-eyes, still she would have been a horrid, grisly brute."

"If I had been a repulsive little girl, instead of a calm bred, affable living, pitiful to the poor lady, that bug-eyed woman had detest me with all her bug heart, still she would have been a horrid, grisly brute".

"If that bug-eyed woman had stood alone in Fiji with no human being to compare her to, still the bug-eyed woman would have been a horrid, grisly brute.

"She has left her horrid bug-mark on my honorable soul. Not anything under the sun can ever blot out the horrid bug-mark from my decent soul. A million curses on the grisly, bug-eyed woman," said Cheryl calmly.

"Then that, for one thing, is not relative," Lynn said. "But maybe that is because of the power your eyes and your decent soul. Where there are no eyes and no honorable souls, at least where the eyes and the decent souls can not be considered as themselves, but only as things without feeling for life, then they are not relative?"

"Nothing is relative," said Cheryl. "If your cat's exquisite fur coat is full of insects and you stroke your cat with your hands, then presently you may amass numbers of the insects. You love the cat, but you do not love the insects. You forgive the insects for the love of the cat, though you hate them no less. So then that is not relative. If that were relative you would love the insects a little for the same reason that you forgive them, for love of your cat.Condone is a weak standard and can have no relevance on your attitude toward the insects."

Cheryl gazed calmly over Lynn's head at the ocean.

When Cheryl mood is that easygoing, she talks courteously evenly and positively, and is beautiful to look at.

Lynn's mind was now in much disorientation upon the relative's subject in question. However, Lynn felt that she must know all that Cheryl thought about it.

"What would you say, Cheryl" said Lynn, "to a case like this: If a soul were at divergence with anything that touches it, I mean everything that makes life, so that it must battle through the nights and days with pungency, is not that because the soul has no sense of fraction, and has not made itself really relative to each and everything that is? relative, so that when one rigid thing touches it, concurrently one mellow thing will touches it, it gives the relative a brilliant pleasure."

"Nothing is relative," again said Cheryl. "Nothing can be relative. Nothing need be relative. If a soul is wearing itself to tiny shreds by grappling days and nights, that is a matter relating eccentric to the soul, and to nothing else, nothing else. If a soul is wearing itself to tiny pieces by grappling, the more fool it. It is scuffling because of things that would never, wrestle because of it. In truth, not one of them would move itself a yard because of so pitiful a thing as a soul."

Lynn looked at Cheryl her hair, straight into her angel eyes. As Lynn looked, she was reminded of the word "eternity."

A human being is a quite unique person, and truly great.

Cheryl is a person who always talk wisely.

Cheryl has reached that triumphant point where a human being predicts nothing. "If the days of a life, Cheryl" Lynn said, "are made bright because of two hearts that are dear to each other, and if the life happens upon a day when the thought of the two whom it loves makes its own heart like paradise?"

"Stupid life," said Cheryl. "There is no sorrow in Fiji like what comes of loving some one with honorable heart. And if the any one is the only thing that life can call its own, then misery to it. It needs things like shelter, belonging, a bit of toughness, clean water, beautiful nature for meditation and holidays trips. Without these necessity one life would be cut short by pure suffering."

Lynn continued probing again. "When all broad highways come together, and all hearts are careful to know what will happen, will there not be one grand modification, and life and all become at once elegantly relative?"

Lynn and Cheryl are akin to each other in a few ways. Each passing day they contemplate together.

One day they were stroll along a stretch of trees, when stood before them a great big iron fence it was so wide it would take them hours to get around it. It was too high for them to jump over the fence. It was too solid to push through it. It seems to end directly across another road.

They stopped for a while and drank some water they carried with them. They sat for almost an hour chatting and giggling.

Lynn became exceeding weary with looking at the great, long and high fence.

"Possibly," says Lynn, "The fence is long and high for a reason. Maybe it's the great wall of town."

"Maybe," says Cheryl "Behind this great fence might be an old forbidden spooky castle."

Cheryl and Lynn's hearts beat high and fast. They wondered, and ponder They walked a bit to their left they came up to a little puddle of clear water, with little ripples.

"It may be," Lynn said, "that this heartening ripple will show us some way to get beyond this fence where things are divine."

"Maybe," says Cheryl "that the heartening ripple will show us something divine among these few things on this side of the fence."

Pleasures cheers us

Oh who can envisage your joy! What we think, or what we do, still our thoughts glance upon our happiness! your lady friend now will be willing, rejections are laid aside. Only there's a little shame and which won't be totally be forgotten, because the union is not yet completed. O those Lovers, who could wish for a greater happiness than they now possess! For what a man will, she will also, and what she fancies, is all your pleasure. You may now tumble in a bed of Roses; for all sour looks, will turn to sweet smiles, and she that used to drive you from her, pulls you now to her. Oh, that beautiful body, which before you dared to touch with your hands and fingers, you may now, without asking clasp by whole handfuls. Certainly, they are at full view, consider all this rightly, O unspeakable pleasure who can disbelief but that you are the happiest man alive?

O victorious lover, don't allow your cheerful mind run too much upon these lustrous things, be a little modest in your desired pleasures, if it might happen that there come some unruly hindrance, for sometimes I've seen, that all those fancy roses, comes with many pricking nettle.

The mouth which at first was hail with so many pleasurable kisses, and appeared as if it had lots of dew from heaven; was compared to be the tongue of an avenger.

A short pleasure tale

Jay and Kym lived in a small town. It was a cheerful, clean town, with wide roads, and an old church that had small trees next to it. Their Jay and Kym house had a beautiful garden behind it, in which they used to play very happily, and run and jump about on the grass plot. They also made many pleasant little excursions into the town, when their brother Karl was able to go with them.

One of their favourite walks was on the weekends through the woods around half a mile from the town. There was a massive Rose manor right next to the end of the woods. It belonged to a prosperous lord; but nobody had lived in it for quite some time. The gardens, the car park, the lawn were, however, kept in fine order; and there was a rumour, that some day the house would be put in repair and furnished. As it was now, people could walk by the paths through the woods close up to it.

One of these footpaths was just outside the facade of the flower garden, and led up to the veranda partly gone to ruin. The door next to the veranda was always closed; but it was so shady and pleasant there, that it was a favourite place for Jay and Kym to play in, while Karl sat under a tree reading; and they would often look up at the beautiful roses,sun flower, Daisy and other creepers that hung over the top of the facade, and wish they might go into the garden and see all the lovely flowers they thought must be there.

They wish to be permitted within the facade, and see not only the beautiful garden, but the Old manor itself, because a young gardener, who was at work for the lord of the manor, had told them a great deal about the manor. This gardener, Trevor, was a close friend of theirs. He made a bunches of all varieties of flowers for them, which they put in the garden, and taught them how to sow seed, mulch the plants, even budding some trees, he would describe the paintings Rose manor hall; and he knew all its wonders quite well, for he had worked there for over a years.

After all this, Kym and Jay were quite pleased, when, one day, Trevor brought them permission to go and see it, from Miss. Susan, the housekeeper, who lived in one of the lodges, close by, and was allowed to show the place to visitors. They thanked Trevor very much for obtaining such a pleasure for them, and then ran to their mama and papa to ask their leave to go, which they gave them directly.

The next day was very sunny and bright, they set out after their early lunch, in high spirits, accompanied by Karl. To add to their pleasure, their mama and papa had told them they might order a donkey-couch in the village, to bring them home. They were both sure the children would be tired on their return; and this was a thing they enjoyed hugely.

The children arrived at the great big Rose manor hall, and rang the bell.

Miss Susan did not keep them waiting long; she open the huge door, she looked at them, greeted them with a smiley, and asked them to come in. She was a traditional little old lady, with a lime green silk gown on, that swished as she moved, and wore a very starched cap and handkerchief.

They liked the inside of the building very much. The floor they trod on was made of squares of marble, and there were seats and a round marble table. A long flight of clean and polished red carpet steps in front of it led down to a broad gravel walk that bounded one end of the flower garden. The garden was uniquely laid out, in an smooth-fashioned style, and the green lawn in the middle looked so smooth and tempting, that they could not resist running down the steps towards it the moment they saw it. Miss. Susan and Karl followed them.

Their feet sank in the fine-textured grass as they walked over it. In the middle there was a large round pond, with a fountain which sprung up into the air and then fell again in showers of sparkling drops, that blustered the surface of the water, and made it peek in the sun as if it were some jewel. It was so clear, that, though it was deep, they could see every blade and leaf of the green moss-grown weeds among the little pebbles at the bottom; and swimming through it two fish. Kym had slices of bread in a paper-bag that her mama and papa had given her in case they should feel hungry before they got home. Miss Susan told Kym the fish would come up to the surface to eat crumbs, she swiftly and excitedly threw some in for them, and up they came, with their bright scales flashed like a flash-camera as they caught the sunlight.

It was some time before the children could leave this cheerful pond, and when they did, they saw A large flower bed, and at all the four corners of the lawn, a small round one. These flower beds were bordered and carefully pegged down made a beautiful setting for the bright flowers within. Tulips, Daffodil, Carnations, Daisy, Marigold, Columbine, Forget-me-not and other lovely things.

Besides these beds, there were at regular distances trees on the lawn, with round bushy heads, full of magnificent flowers of many different shades, sending out the most heavenly scent; and the facade which compassed the gravel walk, and which they had looked at from the outside, was covered with all manner of creepers, honeysuckle, jasmine, passion-flowers, and many others.

Miss Susan led them by a gateway in the facade to a long straight walk, which led under some tall trees, whose thick branches shaded their heads, to the main entrance of the manor hall. She then, with a large key opened the great heavy door, and they all went in.

At first the light, the children eyes had been sparkling by the art work, with beautiful painted glass windows, that threw beautiful colors, purple, red, orange, yellow,blue, and green on the marble floor; and that the stone frames of the windows were carved and decorated, and the stone facades.

Then they went through some large rooms, with walls and ceilings of the same oak decorations, beautifully carved in various shapes and other forms, to represent small animals and fruits, and angels with wings. The children liked the windows better than all; for the walls were so thick that each window seemed to be at the end of a room of its own.

At last, when they had gone through so many rooms, that the children began to keep to tire a bit. However, they heard with joy, that they were next to go into the park at the back of the manor hall, which restored their energy. They followed Miss Susan through a court and an old gateway, and here she wish them farewell. They thank her with all their hearts for her affections, away they ran through the main gate.

It was delightful to see inside the great big Rose manor hall, the children said to each other with cheerfulness.

They walk through a park that took them good while, and the children began to feel tired again; so Karl suggested to them to sit down and rest on the grass, which was all overgrown. While they sat, there Kym, kept thinking of the donkey-chair. After awhile they set off home. They went to the door to see if the donkey chair had come. It was not there yet.

"Don't be despair," said Laura. "If you may wait a little longer donkey-chair might have come."

"I so looking forward for this donkey-ride," Kym replied;

The time had come Kym had just taken her seat in the donkey-chair.

"How tired they look!" said she, as she saw them going slowly on.

"I will run after them and direct them to our house," said Laura.

Much as they liked a drive in the donkey-chair, no drive in the world could have made these children so happy as they felt in their tour of the Rose manor hall. Their hearts filled with joy, they made funny jokes with each other and never thinking of either tiredness, hunger, or thirst.and they were happy and comfortable all their days.

Joy cherish our hearts

You bring me joy. A beautiful song I use to sing to my first ever girlfriend. What a wonderful feeling when you can feel a person's heart. And they can feel yours. Even when you can't see their face you remember their smile.

Joy is such a material like what the hinges of Heaven's doors are made of. So our fore fathers believed. Cheerfulness is the income yielded by a wise investment of one's spirit. On this interest, so long as it flows in regularly, the modest man may live in the land of the Joyful Heart.

No sheer fullness of life will qualify a man for acceptance to the land of the Joyful heart. The joy of living and the up rise of happiness manifest the escalation of passion.

I sometimes marveled if there is any other creativity has ever, in such a short time, made so many joyful hearts as the development of spontaneous music. It has brought radiance, unity, cheerfulness, and the offering of self expression to every houses, villa, castles, and lonely farmhouse near the meadows. Its voice has plainly gone throughout all the earth, and with a velocity more like that of luminosity than of sound.

A brief tale on joy

All day the comfy breeze played with her hair, and the teenage looking face looked out across the water. She was waiting, but she could not tell what she was waiting for.

The sea waves ran up and up on the sand, and ran back again, and colorful sea shells rolled. Life smiling moving on through the day, with the sunlight in her eyes, she bath in the delight of the sun laid closed to the banks of the sea and fell asleep, waiting still.

Then a small boat alight on the sand, and then a few steps were on the shore the teenage looking face awoke and heard it. A comforting hand was laid upon her, and a breathtaking quiver passed through her. The teenage looking face girl looked up, and saw over her the peculiar, adorable eyes of Joy and she thought she must have been waiting to see Joy.

And Joy drew the teenage face girl up to her.

And with that meeting was born a thing scarce and captivating Joy. First she met Joy. The sunlight shone brilliantly upon the enjoyable water. The florets, when turn back their lips for the sunbeam kiss, are so crisp. Each pulses beat brisk. It was so pleasant, so mellow!

Joy and the teenage face girl reveled extraordinarily. They whispered cheerful words to each other, deep in their hearts these simple words, "This will be part of us for ever."

Then there came a time, after a few months? when the thing was not as it had been with Joy and the young face looking girl.

Still it Joy tried to to be cheerful not only for oneself ,but for the other as well. Joy was always laughing, playing, sparkled eyes light up the world.

And Joy and the young face girl kept looking into each other's eyes, and says these magical words, "My dear would you like me to walk with you through paradise?" Each heart whispered these joyous words, "I would very much like to take that journey with you."

One day, the young face girl and Joy went to the sea front they met a friendly stranger, with full open eyes, soft and dismal. Neither noticed it. However, the friendly stranger dejected eyes became a bit warmer, once the conversations got flowing.

The short, soft and dismal eyes stranger got between Joy and the young face girl, into one hand of each, and drew them closer, and walked on between them. Joy looked down in sorrow, she saw her tears reflected in the short stranger dismal eyes. Always its full eyes were sad and thoughtful, always the young face girl was smiling quietly.

The young face girl then took short stranger hands and held them against her beating cheerful heart, and warmed them with a bit of comforting joy.

They came to a part of the sea front into a land of lovely palm trees, strangely the full sad eyes of the friendly stranger lit up, and cheerful dimples broke out upon the face. Brightly laughing, as they walked over the soft green grass, and gathered Lilly flowers and twisted them round their heads, softly laughing all the while. He touched them as their bliss had touched his, but his fingers grip more fondly.

So they stroll on, through beautiful long stretch of land, always with that short valiant smiling one between them. At times they remembered that first radiant moment.

They went to see a fortune teller; that wise old woman who has always one elbow on her knee, and her soft chin in her magical hand, she who diverts brightness out of the past to shine it on the future.

And Joy and the young face girl shouted out, "O wise lady! tell us: when we first met, a lovely brilliant thing belonged to us, cheerfulness with only a few tear, lovely sunshine with nice breeze to shade."

The wise old fortune teller, answered, "Would you give up that which walks beside you now?"

Joy and the young face girl, with affliction "No!"

"Give this up!" said the young face girl. "When my head aces, who will lay their comforting hands upon it? When I'm sad who will warm my freezing heart?"

Joy shouted out, "Let me not lose this bond between us!"

The wise old fortune teller answered, "Love is blind! What you once had is that which you have now! When you two first meet, a shining star was born. When the pathways begin to callous, when the days are rough, and the nights get long and cold, then it begins to change.

The earnest, candied, caring thing, warm in the coldest nights, courageous in the hard times, its name is empathy, which you've shown to each other, it is the perfect love which your hearts will share endlessly.

A happy heart is a cheerful heart

The most imperative motive of all human actions is the desire to be happy. But it is difficult to attain happiness if the search for it is made the constant aim of one's life, although the primordial craving for it is an instinct in our nature.

Unfortunately, in the majority of cases, man does not see clearly the road leading to happiness because he is seeking it in the immediate and complete satisfaction of his desires, in material or intellectual delights whose worth he exaggerates; in superfluity, in possession, in all that he takes for happiness, but which is in reality mere enjoyment allied to fears, dangers, and regrets.

A happy story

What troubles you, Tim?" asked Mrs. Perry, speaking in a tone of caring regard to her husband, who sat temperamental, with his eyes now fixed upon the floor, and now following the forms of his clearly adorn children as they modeled, full of health and spirits, about the room.

It was late evening, and Mr. Perry, a man who earned the family necessities by the sweat of his brow, returned from his daily work.

No answer was made to the Mrs Perry's question. A few minutes went by, and then she asked again:

"What's the matter with you, Tim?"

"Nothing more than normal," Tim replied. "There's always something wrong. The truth is, I'm out of heart."

"Tim!"

Mrs. Perry came and stood beside her husband, and laid her hand calmly upon his shoulder.

The bad spirit of jealousy and unhappiness was in the poor man's heart, this Mrs Perry understood too well. She had repeatedly seen him in this frame of mind.

"I'm as good as I can get; am I not?"

"I hope you can get a great deal better," replied Mrs. Perry.

Mr Perry job made him roll in wealth, while Mrs Perry was impel to work early and late, could scarcely keep soul and body together.

"No, Tim! Don't talk like that. It does you no good. We have a happy home, with food and attires, let us be satisfied and grateful."

"You mean , grateful for this mean hut! Grateful for hard work, meager expense, and uncivil clothing!"

"The happiest of people enjoys their work regardless of the wage package. The happiest of people cook and eat healthy. Do you ever go to bed hungry, Tim?"

"Of course not."

"Do you or the children shiver in the coldest of winter for lack of heating and warm clothing?"

"No; but"…..

"Tim! It is not good to look past your real luxury in envy of the blessings given to others. Think about it, we receive all kinds of good blessings. They will always be people more fortunate and less fortunate than you in this short life, given unto us. With more, you might not be so happy as you are."

"I'll take the risk," said Mr. Perry. "Give me loads of money, and I'll increase the springs of enjoyment."

"The greatest amount of happiness, I believe, is found in that condition wherein the will power had placed us."

"Then every poor man should willingly remain poor!" answered Tim

"Tim, what I'm trying to say is I think every man should seek earnestly to improve his worldly gains. However, be contented with his lot at all times; for only in contentment is true happiness, and this is a kind of blessing the indigent may share equally with the wealthy. In fact, I believe the poor have this blessing in huge store. You, are a happier man than your company's managing director"

"I don't think so."

"Look at his face. Doesn't that tell the true picture? Would you like to swap with him in every honor?"

"No, not in every honor. However, I would like to have his money."

"Ah, Tim! Tim!" Mrs. Perry shook her head. "You are giving place in your heart for the entrance of hateful spirits. Try to appreciate, what you have, and you will be a happier person than your managing director."

"I know. A man who work's as hard as any other, yet, can't help sleeping soundly."

"Then toiling is a blessing."

"'Tim. The company's managing director, has got himself so electrified about business, that he sleeps scarcely five hours in the twenty-four. He doesn't eat or drink healthy enough. His hair is going Grey rapidly due to the stress of running the business. Scarcely a day passes that something does not go wrong. Labourer blunders in their contracts, profits fell below what he forecast them to be, and agents proved deceitful; in fact, numerous amount of things occur to interfere with his forecast, and this overshadowed his brain with disappointment.

We were much happier when we were poorer, Mrs. Perry. There was a time when we relished this life. Bright days! how well are they remembered! We had less wants then than I have ever had since, and was far happier.'"

Suddenly there was a cry that came from the road.

"Pay attention!" exclaimed Mr. Perry.

It was the company's managing director, who was just about to cross the road to grab the telegraph. He was hit by a speeding motorcyclist. His wife screaming aloud neighbors running from all direction to the scene of the accident.

"Poor manager!" Said Tim "I pity him from my very heart!" was his generous, condoling exclamation, as soon as he met the managing director's wife.

"His he insured?" asked Mrs. Perry.

"Yes. The motorcyclist is insured as well. However, He used some of the claim, six months ago for loss of earnings for something else. The price of machinery is now high, and he used that part of the claim to purchase machinery's to help maintain our warehouse production side of the business. I never seen anyone so upset like him before this happened a few minutes ago."

"Poor man! His sleep will not be so sound as yours, tonight, Tim." Mrs Perry said

"He most certainly won't."

"Nor, booming like he use to be, will he be as happy as you tomorrow?"

"If I were as wealthy as he is," said Mr. Perry, "I would not worry myself to death for this minor accident. He's just a bit shaken up. There's no broken bones, no cuts just a minor bruise on his leg. I would, rather, be thankful for the wealth still left in my possession."

Mrs. Perry jolted her head sideways.

"Tim, the same spirit that makes you uneasy and discontented now, would be with you, no matter how better might be your extrinsic circumstances. The manager was once as poor as we are. Do you think he's happier for his wealth? Does he really enjoy life more? Has wealth made him sleep more candidly?"

"And other men, in this fallen and corrupt world, are free from this same shortcoming, Tim. If wealth were pursued for selfless ends, then it would make its beneficiary happy."

Mrs. Perry spoke peacefully, and wisely that was on her mind, it slips its beams upon the mind of Mr Perry.

"They who get wealthy in this world, gets lucky or pass up through ceaseless work and anxiety; and, while they appear to relish all the good things of life, in reality savor but little. They get only their edibles and clothes. I have worked for many wealthy ladies, and I can't remember one who appeared to be happier than I am. And I am mistaken if your experience is not very much like my own."

One day, a few weeks after. Mr Perry came home from his work. As he entered the living room his wife and children sat, the former looked up to him with a cheerful smile of welcome, and the latter converged around him, filling his ears with the music of their happy voices. Mrs Perry drew an arm around one and another, and, as Tim sat in their midst, his heart swelled in his chest, and warmed with a glow of happiness.

Soon the evening meal was served by his gorgeous wife Mrs Perry, the good angel of his courteous home. Mr Tim Perry, as he looked around upon his smiling lovely children, and their soul heart, patient, cheerful mother, felt that he had many blessings for which he should be grateful.

"I've seen something, a short while ago, that I will never forget," said Tim, when alone with his wife.

"What was that, Tim?"

"I had an occasion to call at Mr. Harvey's house, one of the shareholder at work on some work related business, as I came home this afternoon. Mr. Harvey is rich, and I have often envied him; but I refuse to envy him ever again. I found him in his sitting-room, alone, pacing about the floor with a distraught look on his face. He gazed at me with an irritable expression as I entered. I mentioned my work situation, when he said in grumpy and rudely manner.

"'I've got no time to discuss that now.'

"As I was turning away, a door of the room opened, and Mrs. Harvey and the children entered.

"I wish you would send those children up to the play-centre," he bellowed, in a half-angry voice. 'I'm in no mood to be bothered with them now.'

"The look mock-up upon their mother by those innocent little children, as their mother shoved them from the room, I will never forget that scene. I remembered it all, as I left the house, Mr. Harvey was talking to his wife, he'd just lost thousands upon thousands on the market exchange. I am happier than he is tonight."

"And happier you may ever be Tim. Once you stoop to the courteous flowers that spring up along your path of life."

Cheerful letters for cheerful hearts

Love breathed a secret to her listening heart,

love said "Be quite."

And abide as one within this world,

Yet the moon and star seemed by their secret lit.

Where she passed, each whispering wind blow,

And Each little blossom in the flower,

Called joyously to her, "don't worry, be happy"

Life grew so radiant, and so lavish,

She felt a peculiar ecstasy in her soul.

Then, after heartache, came the supreme bliss

They brought beautiful angel, for a kiss!

Love starts with a small beat in the heart,

Love is born in an attraction sometimes in three words,

That tiny glint that burns in our hearts.

Love is not just a word, it is also a promise,

the promise words say I love you,

With one's heart trembling?

You bring so much joy to my heart

which is why my heart is always dancing.

Let my heart slipped into you.

It seems, also, that you are the shining star

And that I am at the top of a mountain.

If I had wings like a dove

I would fly to you with beautiful rose in my mouth,

And with juicy kisses of like a holy bird at your petal door.

It is hard for anyone to tell

The masked thoughts in another person heart,

If you could inside a woman's heart

peel to your eyes lids,

Her heart is so divine,

That her love burns from afar.

See you have love in heart and a girl like one of the angels

 Yes angels do exist

And lat your burdens on her shoulders

Yes burdens exist

Live each day as if it's you last and forget about hell

I don't know if hell exist

There's a promise land waiting for us, it's fill with paradise

I believe paradise exist

My heart plays no more with life,

it has found a beautiful princess the moonlight;

The flower of her face is growing in my heart

I feel her sunlight all around,

I see her angel eyes in my dreams

And there is dew on the petal flowers that live within my heart

May your sparkling eyes, your eyes of summer, I see each day in the name of love

Let our sparked souls keep flaming in the name of love.

May my heart against your heart be for you here on earth in the name of love

Let us live like two wild teenagers in the name of love

May we grow Grey and old together in the name of love

When the starry sky covers our hearts,

so may feel a greater and more passion stirring within us.

The bright silver stars follow their courses high up in the sky;

and the calm is so great that the great sea listens,

our hearts beat so strongly that they make all things glistens

With the same love that you were for me long ago

Copies of our love shaded the pretty roses, in our garden,

Our hearts are centred there.

Your brightness and your movements assembling the flowers of our hearts'

It keep my happiness warm there within your folded arms;

your cheerful words, in their sing still with great a charm.

The silver threads that slip their waving ways through your glossy hair.

You never grumble,

and you believe firmly that true love never dies

when love receives its needs,

the living fire on which our soul feeds

consumes every loss to escalate its spark.

O princess stars, elect of all the spheres

I ask by all thy hopes and fears,

by thy face, the oracle of a soul-mate,

Is this thy unhappiness

O thou captain of superior?

Or does thou weep to know moons

Is still shining down on us saying things are gonna get even brighter

How great my joy!

Which keep in my sight.

I call thee mine,

I share with thee immense happiness

We see the soul, in its earliest light,

It is the soul of thee, and no other form,

Our soul, the star beyond it in the deep

The faith, is large, and warm!

Our cheerful hearts

It does not take a great deal to make two hearts beat faster than one. The heart can misguide itself when it cannot seduce another. Which will be cold pleasures to some lovers, though it may cheer others.

To admit a divine guest into the inner parts of the human heart. Remember, too, that you can never expect an angel to act as a housekeeper; the sweeping must be done by the individual. And, unless each heart is given access to the other, their bonding is false, perhaps risky.

No man can tell to whom a woman's heart belongs; not even the man who calls the woman his sweetheart. Let no man envisage that when he has won himself a woman, he has won that woman's heart. Sometimes a woman will give her heart to one man and her pledge to another. Many hearts are hard to read especially if it is a coating. That must be a curious love that causes the heart to stumble.

A lot of men has talk over, for years whether to propose or not; and sometimes a woman will accept the man that she refused frankly a few months before. Maybe, where the heart ponders, it is not so much a case of love as a case of comfort. For, an engulfed love leaves the heart of either distrust.

Love is the only known means by which the individual heart can make any growth whatsoever beyond its own confines.

The heart be it human's or any insects is the core of its self-created domain. Some day, perhaps, man's sphere will extend as far beyond the stars as today it extends beyond the ranges.

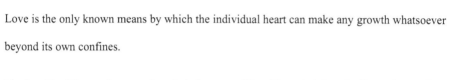

There is a Universe, is apparent; that it is one and complete, we suppose; that our human hearts enthuse mutual support, sympathy, love, friendship, wife, husband,brothers, brothers, and companionship.

It is quite impossible to perceive of a Universe of love, in which all the claims of heart and soul and Senses shall be eternally and infinitely satisfied? Nevertheless, on this planet earth. He who is commander of his soul, can rise above nemesis.

A lesson our human heart has to learn. the human heart needs to give cheerfulness, kindness, joys, genuine laughter,the glad tidings list goes on.

Health cheers our hearts

Health is the most valuable of all possessions, for with health one can attain anything else within reason. A few of the great people of the world have been sickly, but it takes men and women sound in body and mind to do the important work. Healthy men and women are a nation's most valuable asset.

It is natural to be healthy, but we have deviated so far astray that illness is the rule and good health the exception. Of course, a lot of people are well enough to attend to their work, but nearly all are suffering from some illness, mental or physical, acute or chronic, which denies them a part of their strength. The average individual is of less worth to himself, to his family and to society than he could be. His bad habits, of which he is often not aware, have brought weakness and illness upon him. These conditions prevent him from doing his best mentally and physically.

Everything that is beneficial must be paid for in some way and the price of continued good health is some fundamental knowledge and self-control. There are no hardships connected with rational living. It means to live comparatively and somewhat more simply than is customary. clarity reduces the amount of work and friction and adds to the enjoyment of life. The cheerfulness, the happiness and the tingling with the joy of life that come to those who have perfect health more than compensate for the pet bad habits which must be given up.

No one can cover the field of health completely, for though it is very simple, it is as big as life. The most important single item for clinching and retaining physical health is proper feeding. Dietetics should be the principal subject of study. It should be approached both from the scientific and from the empirical side. It is not a rigid subject, but one which can be treated in a very elastic way. The scientific part is important, but the practical part, which is the art, is exceedingly more important. A part of the art of feeding and fasting is scientific, for we get the same results every time, under given conditions.

To consider the fact that the body is made up of numerous tissues, such as connective tissue, blood, nerves and muscles; that these in turn are made up of billions of cells, as are the various glandular organs and membranes; that these cells are continuously bathed in blood and lymph, from which they select the food they need and throw the refuse away, we can wonder that an organism so complex is so resistant, stable and strong.

For a balanced diet we need some building food, protein; some force food, starch, sugar and fat; some of the mineral salts in organic form, best derived from raw fruits and vegetables; and a medium in which the foods can be dissolved, water.

Cheerfulness and cognition

We all enter the world with plenty of nerve energy, and by protecting that energy we can adapt and regulate our nerve equipment to keep pace with the progress and evolution of our times. A way in which we can maintain and conserve nerve equilibrium and strength is by resting and relaxing the nerves each day. We could take a few minutes each evening and using the time for sizing up things, by inventory, analysis, speculation, comparison and hypothesis

When the day's work is over, if you can try and spend around twenty minutes each evening in seclusion, and with closed eyes, size yourself up. Think over your daily round and the work you are doing. Are you getting the best out of yourself? Or are you plodding along aimlessly, scattering your energy in a random, hit-or-miss fashion that benefits nobody? Are you growing, or are you standing still? In these twenty minute sizing-up sessions, you will come to grips with yourself. You will see yourself as you really are, and will discover your weaknesses, your strength, and your real worth.

Make yourself right before you criticize another person. Ask yourself this question, "Am I pleasant to live with?" Be pleasant to live with and you will have more pleasant things to live for.

There will be kindnesses, kisses, beauty, health, peace, fun, happiness and content coming your way all along the great big road of life you are traveling.

Be pleasant in your home. Making children feel at home is the most gratifying feeling on earth. Every act and example is written in the child's memory tablet. Let your hours with the children be loving, laughing, living hours. Pat them on the head, joke with them, whisper affection, express love to them. Those acts will be remembered in all their years to come, for you are planting everlasting plants that will flourish on to generations and make children happy a thousand years from now.

It is hard enough to do duty once, but doubly hard when you expect mentally everything you have to do tomorrow. Doing things twice is a pattern easily obtained if you don't watch out, and it means wasted energy. A tired mind is harder to rest than a tired body, so we must squeeze this advanced mental work in the bud.

Wisdom has proved that nerves cannot be reinstated by dope, patent medicines, tonics or prescriptions. The healing must come by and through the individual possessing the nerves, and by and through the individual's power of will and mastery of the mind. Get the mental equipment right. Let the mind master the body. Let the nerve sufferer get hold of him or herself and fill their brain with faith-thought instead of fear-thought, with boldness instead of weakness, with strength instead of frailty, with hope instead of anguish, with smiles instead of frowns, with occupation instead of laziness, and wonders will appear. The little frazzled, prickling nerve-ends will then start to synchronize instead of fight, to harmonize instead of breaking into strife, to build instead of destroy.

Your nerves can be posed, your thoughts elevated, your health reimposed, your ambition re-established, your normality secured. Smiles, love and content are to be yours. Poise, efficiency, peace, your blessings. Health, happiness and hope will be your dividends.

There are magnificent valuable things for us to do, and with continuity of action and singleness of purpose on our part the days will pass by as we are seizing opportunity and making use of the things required for the fulfillment of our desires. We are like the coral insect that takes from the running tide the material to build a well grounded fortress. Our running tide is made up of the gliding golden days. Let's waste no time in trying to make friends or in seeking to attach ourselves to others. True friends are not caught by pursuit; they come to us; they happen through circumstances we do not create.

Independence is ours, and we must first use it for our own improvement. We will then have an excess of energy to allow us to help others. Our energy hours must be committed to our purposes and conducts. At times, we can try to rest and relax, and repair the waste that energy-consuming makes. Breathe good air, laze in the sunshine, see nature, and say to yourself: "All these treasures are mine; all these things I am part of."

Try not to think too much of death, or waste time preparing for it. It makes us miserable each day. It makes us fragile and fills us with worry, and it draws the day of our departure nearer. Today is ours. Live freely, fully for today. Be lion heart, unhurried, and undisturbed. We are building temperament, and the way we build it is by mental perspective, by our acts, and by the way we employ the valuable moments of today. Put yourself in harmony with nature, realize the wonderful force of your will, and you will be robust, a genuine king or queen among men.

You can change your thoughts to boldness, optimism, and good cheer, and busy your hands with work. Think of the happiness spells you have had, and know that there are more happiness rewards coming to you. Keep hold of these thoughts, and with it, a useful situation, and the sunshine will eliminate your gloomy uneasiness and sorrow, thoughts like the sun banish the April showers, bringing about a more beautiful day because of the clouds and storms just passed.

Envy no one; envy breeds worry. The person you would envy has his sorrows and shadows, too. You see him only when the sunlight is on his face; you don't see the person when the person is in shadow land. You can be happy often, and when you are not happy, just seem to be happy anyway; it will help you a great deal.

Many of the people you envied in the past are dead, buried or cremated. Many of the people you envy now inside their heart are miserable, and you wouldn't envy them if you could look through the artificial outside and know their real hidden thoughts and lives. You are all right; you have far more blessings than sorrows. You can never be entirely free from troubles, care or little irritations.

You are hurt when it comes to judging yourself. You compare your frailty with your friends' solidity, and this comparison is unfair; it makes you lose confidence. Always express faith, tenacity, and cheer thoughts, whether you feel them or not. Do this heroically and tenaciously, and soon the fear, shadows and blemish feelings will leave you, and you will be in reality sturdy, courageous, dynamic, and will do things you never thought possible.

Get hold of your thoughts; make yourself think up, and have hope and fearlessness. Hold on to your determination. You will flourish, you will have poise, and every once in a while happiness will come as a reward. No man will be more surprised at your complete change of attitude and character than yourself.

The practice of medicine in the past has been directed towards the curing of disease and physical ailments already developed. The practice of medicine in the future is to be along preventive lines. Science is showing us how to prevent infection. Science is fighting the deadly bacterium which comes to us in the air we breathe, the water we drink, and the food we eat, and the septic things we touch.

Nature has supplied the human body with a home guard of necessary bacteria, and in the circulation system are phagocytes which fight the overwhelming viruses and by and large destroy them. When the system is weakened through disease, through lack of exercise, or through improper food, disease has an easy time.

Anger makes weak stomachs, giddy heads, poor judgment, lost friends, despair and illness, and if the pattern becomes substantiated, will likely lead to thrombosis. When two men have differences, watch the cool man finish victoriously, the angry man always loses. Keep a cool head and let the other fellow anguish and fume. He will tie himself up in a knot, and when the chime is rung, he will be the loser.

Do not think for one minute that you can go through life without your share of pain, disillusion, obstacles and disappointment. It can't be done. No human being has ever done it. Clouds will come, but they can be dispersed. Stumbling blocks will arise, but they can be overcome. Troubles will visit you, but meet them boldly and courageously and do not show cold feet.

To the thinking human, life is a great arena wherein good and bad, joy and sorrow, faith and disillusion, happiness and unhappiness, success and failure are inseparably combined. The joy and happiness, take on gratefully; the sorrow and disillusion, bear with resilience. And remember, although it is not possible to enjoy an absolute and continued state of happiness, it always lies within your power to have calmness, poise, peace and contentment.

Only to the thinking human is it given to see life and see it whole. He only has the true sense of proportion. He keeps his eye on the main purpose, fixed in the realization that he is the master of himself and commander of his own soul. He is self-reliant, for he knows that no matter what emerges, he carries happiness and contentment within himself wherever he goes. The practice of thinking is a tower of strength that reinforces your mind of resistance and makes you stronger.

No need for haste be calm and cheerful

How can anyone do anything well while in a never-ending state of rush? How can anyone see anything clearly while in a continual state of rush? How can anyone expect to keep healthy and strong while in a perpetual state of rush?

If we observe ourselves carefully with an impulse to find the hurry proneness, and to find it thoroughly, in order to banish it, you will be surprised to see how much of it there is in you. As we get rid of all the crude forms of hurry, we find in ourselves other hurry habits that are finer and more elusive, and gradually our standards of quiet, deliberate ways get higher; we become more sensitive to hurry, and a hurried way of doing things grows more and more disagreeable to us.

Take a look at the work staff coming out of a manufacturer in the evening hour or at five thirty PM. They are almost tumbling over each other in their hurry to get away. They are putting on their jackets, pushing in their hatpins, and running along as if their evening meal were running away from them.

The tension of hurrying makes contractions in the brain and body with which it is impossible to work freely and easily or to attain as much as might be done without such contractions. The hassle of hurry confuses the brain so that it is impossible for it to expand to an unbiased point of view. The tightness of hurry so contracts the whole nervous and muscular systems that the body can take neither the nourishment of food nor of fresh air as it should.

Often times our days seems so full, and one is so pressed for time that it is impossible to get in all there is to do, and yet a little quiet thinking will show that the important things can be easily put into two thirds of the day, and the remaining third is free for rest, or play, or both. Then again, there is real pleasure in quietly fitting one thing in after another when the day must be full, and the result at the end of the day is only healthy fatigue from which a good night's rest will recharge us entirely.

There is one thing that is very apparent, a feeling of hurry delays our work, it does not hasten it, and the more quietly we can do what is before us, the more quickly and robustly we do it.

The first essential is to find ourselves out, to find out for a fact when we do hurry, and how we hurry, and how we have the sense of hurrying with us all the time. Having readily, and happily, found ourselves out, the treatment is straight before us. Nature is on the side of breathing space and will come to our assistance with higher standards of quiet, the possibilities of which are always in every one's brain, if we only look to find them.

Emotions helps been cheerful

Whether we believe it or not, the fact remains that we ourselves decide which of all the possible emotions we shall choose, or we decide not to press the button for any emotion at all. To a very large degree man, if he knows how and really wishes, may select the emotion which is suitable in that it leads to the right conduct, has an instrumental effect on the body, transforms him to his social environment, and makes him the kind of man he wants to be.

Since this test of emotion is essentially sound, it is not surprising that the nervous man is in a state of distress. Indigestion, fatigue, over-sensibility, sound like problems in physiology, but we cannot go far in the discussion of any of them without coming face to face with the emotions as the real factors in the case. When we turn to the mental facets of nervous folk, we even more quickly find ourselves in the centre of an emotional disturbance. Worried, fearful, anxious, self-pitying, excitable, or sad, the nervous person proves that whatever else a neurosis may be, it is, in essence, a riot of emotions.

But it is not the nervous person only who needs a better understanding of his emotional life. A fortunate man also gets angry for childish reasons; he is biased and malicious, unhappy and sceptical for the very same reason as is the nervous man. Since the working-capital of energy is limited to a definite amount, the control of the emotions becomes a central problem in any life, a deciding factor in the output and the outcome, as well as in comfort and happiness by the way.

Nothing is harder for the average man to believe than this reality that he really has the power to choose his emotions. He has been disgruntled with himself in his past reactions, and yet he has not known how to change them. His vexation or his depression has appeared so undesirable to his best judgment and to his conscious reason that it has seemed to be not a part of himself at all but an annexation from which has swept over him without his consent and quite beyond control.

Although we choose our emotions, we choose in many cases in response to a buried part of ourselves of which we are wholly unaware, or only half-aware. When we do not like what we have chosen, it is because the conscious part of us is out of harmony with another part and that part is doing the choosing. If the emotions which we choose are not those that the whole of us, or at least the conscious, would want, it is because we are choosing in response to hidden impulses, and giving contentment to cravings which we have not perceived. Repeated satisfaction of such desires is responsible for the emotional patterns which we are too likely to consider an inevitable part of our personality, inherited from ancestors who are not on hand to defend themselves. When we form the habit of being scared of things that other people do not fear, or of being displeased or saddened, or of giving way to fits of temper, it is because these habit-reactions persuade the inner cravings that in the circumstances can get fulfillment in no better way.

At any moment an emotion quite out of keeping with conscious wish is allowed to become persistent, we may know that it is being chosen by a part of the personality which needs to be discovered and squarely faced. Nervous symptoms and amplified emotionalism are alike evidence of the fact that the wrong part of us is doing the choosing and that the will needs to be enlightened on what is taking place in the outer edge of its dominions In the choice between emotionalism and calmness, the selection of the former can only be in response to unrecognized desire.

The cheerful goodbye letter

Love to us when we first met, was like two lonely hearts meeting. The planet followed our heart, body, and soul, out of all the people in the world I can't believe your mine.

Our love is so beautiful, that nothing can go wrong There's a great shining glow from your gorgeous smile, makes me taste love like a stimulating divine.

Their hearts are like king and queen sitting on a shining star with both hearts filed with fire and crazy desire

Deep down inside, it's more than fantasy it's really time for love.

There is no standard that strives more good, is of higher service to human's during their journey of the common life, than the heart and the soul that goes out in an all enfolding love for all, that is the inventor of a genuine, cheerful, compassionate and boldness that is not disarrange by the passing manifestation big and small, but that is composed, pleasant, and triumphant to the end, that is finding the best, and that is motivating the best in all. There is no quality that when genuine brings such wealthy returns to its master by ethics feelings that it encourages with their peaceful, inspiring, holistic influences for you.

Always think and hold thoughts of love in heart, and you will love and will be loved

The human life that goes out in love to others is the life that is full, meaningful, rich, and constantly increasing in beauty and in power. The power of every life, the very life itself, is regulated by what it connects itself to.

Tell me how much a person loves and I will tell you how cheerful his or her heart is. Love is the key to a cheerful life, it is the relish of true stimulation to a life worth living. Love makes our heart, soul, and spirit pure and true.

Cheerfulness has a magnificent power. It give us real pleasure when another welcomes us with a cheerful smile. It warms our hearts, it inspires our thoughts, it makes us feel bliss, it makes our eyes sparkle with delight, it makes our faces radiant. Within you there's a power of cheerfulness, let it shine all over the world.